RYA p

Revised and updated 2004
by Jonathan Mendez

Published by
The Royal Yachting Association
RYA House Ensign Way Hamble
Southampton SO31 4YA
Tel: 0845 345 0400
Fax: 0845 345 0329
Email: info@rya.org.uk
Web: www.rya.org.uk

Foreword

Welcome to the exciting sport of Powerboating. The RYA Powerboat scheme meets the training needs of both recreational and professional powerboat operators alike. Whether you are an amateur with a keen sense of adventure or use powerboats as part of your job the RYA Powerboat program will train you in all aspects of safe boat handling and navigation. Adopted by many countries,RYA powerboat courses remain the most popular in the world.

Paul Mara

RYA Chief Powerboat Instructor

Contents

This book is effective for courses from 1 January 2004

INTRODUCTION

RYA Training

One of the strengths of the RYA is its training schemes for all aspects of boating, from windsurfing to offshore cruising. The principle underlying each of these schemes is *Education rather than Legislation*, because we believe that a higher standard of competence can be achieved by voluntary training, rather than legislation requiring registration and driver licensing. You can support this principle by your involvement in the RYA National Powerboat Scheme.

The courses described in this publication are run at RYA Recognised Training Centres in the UK and abroad. RYA recognition is your safeguard that you will be taught by experienced, qualified instructors in suitable, seaworthy boats, to the syllabuses given.

Before a Powerboating school, club or centre can gain RYA recognition, it is inspected to ensure that certain minimum standards are met. Regular and spot inspections ensure that these same standards are maintained.

Full details of RYA recognition and instructor training are given in the *Powerboat Instructors' Handbook* G19. For a list of centres visit the RYA's website www.rya.org.uk or ring 0845 345 0377 for a free copy of this brochure.

Other water users

If you are the driver of a high-speed powerboat, you have a great responsibility towards other water users. The RYA Powerboat Scheme has been developed to advise you of that responsibility at the same time as training you to handle your boat in a seamanlike manner, so that you and your passengers can all enjoy being afloat.

Powerboat drivers sometimes attract publicity, often through lack of awareness of the basic rules and customs of the sea. You can help to redress the balance by courteous driving and by displaying a skillful approach to boat handling.

RYA membership

If you are not already a member of the RYA, we would be delighted to welcome you aboard. We deal with all aspects of boating and have a lot to offer. You'll find more details on pages 41 to 44 of this book.

Powerboating abroad

Many other countries require the owners or drivers of powerboats to hold a certificate of competence, even if only visiting the country for a holiday. To meet this requirement, the RYA issues the International Certificate of Competence, which you will need if you intend to take your boat abroad. The RYA National Powerboat Certificate, Level 2 is the standard required. Contact one of our Training Centres or the RYA for an application form.

Powerboaters with special needs

Recognising that some powerboaters with disabilities are unable to complete the full requirements for an RYA course completion certificate without additional help, the scheme makes provision for certificates to be endorsed as appropriate. The endorsement will indicate the sections of the syllabus for which the powerboater requires assistance.

RYA NATIONAL POWERBOAT SCHEME

The National Powerboat Scheme is applicable to sportsboats, RIBs, dories and launches, and other boats which do not normally provide accommodation or cooking facilities. Training on boats with accommodation is covered by the RYA Motor Cruising Scheme explained in logbook G18.

The lower age limit for RYA powerboat courses is 8 years but the RYA would not recommend under 16s being left in charge of a powerboat without adult supervision.

Full details of the Scheme are given in this handbook:

Level 1	provides a practical introduction to boat handling skills.
Level 2	provides the skills and background knowledge needed by the competent powerboat driver and is the basis of the International Certificate of Competence.
Intermediate Day Cruising	covers practical use of pilotage and passage planning by day on coastal waters, using both traditional and electronic navigational techniques.
Advanced Day & Night	provides the skills and background knowledge needed by powerboat drivers operating by day or night in known or unfamiliar waters, the skipper's role and boat handling in more demanding conditions.
Safety Boat	provides the skills required when acting as an escort craft, safety boat or coach boat for a fleet of dinghies, windsurfers or canoes and for racing or training activities

The syllabi

The following pages describe the syllabus for each level of RYA powerboat course. Due to time constraints and variations in course locations and equipment, not all subjects can be covered in great detail or practically on the water. We have therefore specified three levels of teaching to show you in how much depth you can expect each item to be covered.

These three levels are:

KNOWLEDGE of the subject.

The subject will be briefly explained. Familiarisation during the course and information on where to find out more.

UNDERSTANDS the subject.

The subject will be covered in greater depth and you will be asked to demonstrate a basic understanding and go away from the course able to further develop your own skill in this area. Confirmation of your understanding of the subject may be achieved in a number of ways, such as a short quiz near the end of the course.

CAN demonstrate a level of proficiency in the subject.

The subject will be covered in great depth, including background theory, practical demonstrations by the instructor and repeated practice by yourself until you can demonstrate good skills in this subject.

The course structures are shown on the next two pages.

RYA NATIONAL POWERBOAT SCHEME

LEVEL 1

INTRODUCTION TO POWERBOATING

Preparation •launching and recovering •safety equipment •pre-start checks •personal buoyancy

Boat handling and manoeuvres
•starting and stopping •use of kill cord •steering controls •securing to a buoy •leaving and coming alongside •being towed

Theory and background
IRPCS •ropework •awareness of other water users

LEVEL 2

NATIONAL POWERBOAT COURSE

Preparation •launching and recovering •safety equipment •lines and fenders •fuel tanks

Boat handling and manoeuvres
•effects of current or tide •high and low speed manoeuvring •propeller controls •securing to a buoy •anchoring •leaving and coming alongside •man overboard

Theory and background
•types of craft and engine •maintenance checks •IRPCS •weather forecasts •emergency action

RYA/MCA ADVANCED POWERBOAT CERTIFICATE OF COMPETENCE

Pre-exam experience:
2 years relevant experience including night pilotage. As a guide: 30 days, 2 days as skipper, 800 miles, 12 night hours.

For holders of the Advanced Powerboat course completion certificate:
20 days, 2 days as skipper, 400 miles, 12 night hours.

Form of examination:
Practical exam lasting 4-5 hours for one candidate, up to 7 hours for 2 or 3 candidates.

Certification required before examination:
VHF/SRC Operator's licence, valid first aid certificate.

See pages 29-32 for full details.

INTERMEDIATE

POWERBOAT DAY CRUISING COURSE

Preparation •pilotage •navigation •fuel and engine checks

Boat handling and manoeuvres
•effect of waves and rougher conditions
•power trim and trim tabs
•berthing in differing situations
•use of GPS in high speed navigation and pilotage by day
•It is strongly recommended that candidates hold a first aid certificate and a VHF operator's certificate.

ADVANCED

POWERBOAT DAY AND NIGHT COURSE

Preparation •passage planning •meteorology •skipper's responsibilities

Boat handling and manoeuvres
•high speed boat handling •advanced manoeuvres •manoeuvring in rough weather •chart plotters and radar
• pilotage by day and night
•emergency situations •differences for a twin engine vessel
•You are required to hold a first aid certificate and a VHF operator's certificate.

SAFETY BOAT COURSE

Preparation •safety equipment •assistance with race management •crew communication

Boat handling and manoeuvres
•positioning in respect to fleet •standing off another craft •coming alongside under way •dinghy (including high performance) and windsurfer rescue •towing •mark laying

Theory and background
•rescue of other water users
•communication •VHF •first aid

YOUR POWERBOAT CHECK LIST

Tell someone where you are going and when you plan to return and inform them when you have returned

Listen to the weather forecast
If in doubt, don't go out

Before going afloat check
Personal and boat buoyancy
Alternative means of propulsion
Anchor, chain and warp
Bucket, bailer or bilge pump
Fuel, including reserve tank
First aid kit
Sharp knife
Engine emergency spares
Fire extinguisher
Flares as appropriate
VHF radio
Compass, electronic aids and charts when necessary
Car and trailer are properly parked

When afloat
Keep a good lookout at all times
Don't overload your boat
Obey speed limits in harbours/estuaries etc
Keep to the right in rivers/narrow channels
When crossing a channel, cross quickly at right angles
Keep clear of swimmers, fishermen, canoeists, dinghy sailors, windsurfers and boats/small buoys flying Code Flag A (I have a diver down)
Think how your wash will affect others
Look out for deteriorating weather conditions

On the road remember
Secure boat to trailer and stow all loose gear
Cover your propeller with a prop bag
Trailer lights must repeat those on the rear of the car, including a rear fog light if fitted to the car
The maximum speed limits are 50mph on single carriageways, 60mph on dual carriageways and motorways
Never use the third lane on motorways
Allow extra braking distance if your trailer is unbraked
Corner and reverse with care
Park your car and trailer clear of slipways and above the high water mark
Use the correct number plate

Level 1 Introduction to Powerboating

Aim: To provide a practical introduction to boat handling and safety in powerboats.

The course may be conducted in a variety of boat types, both planing and displacement, and the certificate issued will be endorsed to show the type(s) of boat in which the training took place. The ratio of students to instructors should not exceed 3:1.

Duration: 1 day

Minimum age: 8.

8 to 11 year olds will receive the Level 1 certificate which will be endorsed - *The holder should only use powered craft under the supervision of a responsible adult on board the craft.*

12 to 16 year olds will receive a Level 1 certificate which will be endorsed - *The holder should only use powered craft under the supervision of a responsible adult.*

Section A

Practical boat handling

Launch and recovery (8 to 11 year olds to observe this session only)

Knowledge of:

Considerations to be taken during the launch

The use of a trailer or launching trolley

Considerations to be taken regarding sea conditions and hazards

Construction, width and condition of ramp/slipway

Signature of Instructor

Preparation of boat and crew

Understands:

Personal buoyancy and appropriate clothing

The use of the following equipment: lines, fenders, anchor and warp, bailer, fire extinguisher, pump, paddles or oars, compass, flares, torch, whistle, charts, first aid kit, sharp knife.

Can:

Perform the following: fasten to a cleat and stow an anchor

Signature of Instructor

Boat Handling

Knowledge of:

Planing boats: propeller angle and immersion, use of shallow drive

Low speed handling: ahead and astern

Displacement boats: handling ahead and astern, carrying way in neutral

continued overleaf

Understands:

How to carry out pre-start checks, including fuel tank and fuel bulb

Steering, controls and windage

Can:

Steer and control boat speed

Start and stop the engine

Demonstrate the use of an appropriate length kill cord at all times

Signature of Instructor

Picking up and securing to a mooring buoy

Knowledge of:

Preparation of mooring warps

Use of a boat hook

Method of approach

Crew communication

Making fast

Signature of Instructor

Leaving and coming alongside

Knowledge of:

Wind effect

Approach in tidal stream or current

Understands:

Leaving – ahead or astern

Can:

Demonstrate the use of painter, lines and fenders, attachment to boat, stowage under way

Control speed and angle of approach

Make fast alongside

Signature of Instructor

Being towed

Knowledge of:

Preparing own lines for towing

Accepting a tow

Securing tow lines

Trim and balance under tow

Signature of Instructor

Section B

Theory

Knowledge of:

Loading and balancing the boat and the effect on handling and performance

Local Byelaws and Insurance

Understands:

Crew numbers: minimum number in the boat, keeping a look-out

Awareness of other water users, including effect of wash

Application of IRPCS. Understands rules 5,6, and conduct around commercial shipping in confined waters

Signature of Instructor

Level 2 National Powerboat Course

Aim: To teach boat handling and seamanship in powerboats.

The course may be conducted in a variety of boat types, both planing and displacement, and the certificate issued will be endorsed to show the type(s) of boat in which the training took place. The ratio of students to instructors should not exceed 3:1.

Duration: 2 days

Minimum age: 12

12 to 16 year olds will receive a Level 2 certificate which will be endorsed - *The holder should only use powered craft under the supervision of a responsible adult.*

Section A
Practical

Launching and recovery

Knowledge of:

- Use of a trailer or launching trolley
- Consideration of launching and sea conditions, including hazards and obstructions
- Number of persons required to launch/recover
- Construction, width and condition of slipway
- Steep/slippery slipways, beach launching, lee shores
- Care of trailer bearings, hitch, lashings, ties, lights and winch
- Trailer parking

Can:

- Prepare the boat, lines, fenders, safety equipment, fuel tanks, lines and secure gear on board

Signature of Instructor

Boat handling

Knowledge of:

- Loading: effect on handling and performance, effect on balance and trim, CE Plate and manufacturer's recommendation
- Displacement boats: handling ahead and astern, carrying way

Understands:

- Crew members: minimum number in high speed craft, keeping a look-out

continued overleaf

Awareness of other water users, including effect of wash

Steering, controls, effect of current or tidal stream

High speed manoeuvring: planing, trim tabs and power trim

Planing boats: propeller angle and immersion, shallow drive, high/low speed handling, tiller/console steering

Can:

Carry out pre-start checks, engine starting and stopping

Demonstrate the use of an appropriate length kill cord at all times

Carry out low speed manoeuvres including: turning in a confined area, effect of wind on bow and holding off. Demonstrate an awareness of the danger of flooding when going astern

Carry out high speed manoeuvres including S-turns and U-turns

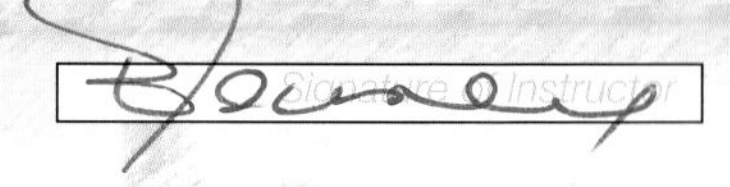

Securing to a buoy

Understands:

Preparation of mooring warp

Use of a boat hook

Method of approach

Crew communication

Making fast

Procedure when overshooting

Can:

Approach and secure to buoy

Signature of Instructor

Anchoring

Understands:

Method of approach in various conditions

Taking way off

Crew communication

Check holding

Depth of water, holding ground, scope required

Knowledge of:

Types of anchor

Stowage and attachment to boat

Preparation of anchor, chain and warp

Weighing anchor

Can:

Approach and anchor correctly

Weigh anchor correctly

Signature of Instructor

Leaving and coming alongside

Understands:

Preparation and use of painter, lines and fenders, attachment to boat, stowage under way

Speed and angle of approach

Wind effect

Method of approach in tidal stream or current

Can:

Make fast alongside

Use springs

Leave – ahead or astern

Signature of Instructor

Man overboard

Knowledge of:

Recovery of man overboard

Can:

Take immediate action

Observe the man overboard

Carry out the correct return with awareness of propeller

Approach and recover the man in the water

Signature of Instructor

Section B

Theory

Knowledge of:

Types of craft: advantages and disadvantages of different hull forms with respect to sea keeping ability

Engines and drives: advantages and disadvantages of outboard, inboard and outdrive units, single and twin screws, choice and use of fuels

Siting of fuel tanks, fuel lines, batteries, wiring, fire extinguishers

Routine engine maintenance checks, basic fault diagnosis

Close down procedure

continued overleaf

Advice to inland drivers about coastal waters

Use and limitations of GPS

Application of local byelaws, especially around commercial shipping

Sources of weather information

Understands:

Awareness of other water users

Communication with other craft – hand and sound signals

Disabled craft

Emergency action, preventing sinking

Adrift – alternative means of propulsion

Towing and being towed

Fire precautions and fire fighting

Ropework

Distress signals and the Mayday call

Can:

Apply IRPCS, principally rules 5, 7, 8, 9, 12-19

Signature of Instructor

Section C
Coastal

Knowledge of:

Pilotage and passage planning

CG66 Small Craft Safety Scheme

Understands:

Charts, chart symbols, buoyage systems

Tides and tidal streams

Can:

Use steering and hand bearing compasses

Apply Section A on coastal waters

Signature of Instructor

Section D

Direct assessment for experienced powerboat drivers

The candidate should have the equivalent of at least one full season's powerboat handling experience.

The candidate must complete the practical exercise described overleaf, and satisfactorily answer questions on Section B.

Candidates seeking assessment on coastal waters will demonstrate a knowledge and practical application of Section C.

Practical assessment of all candidates for Level 2

The practical exercise detailed in the diagram overleaf shows the manoeuvres required to be demonstrated during the practical assessment. Candidates are expected to show that they understand the principles of each manoeuvre. Failure to successfully complete a manoeuvre at the first attempt will not necessarily result in overall failure, but a timely awareness of the need to abort an exercise and try again is important.

Level 2 test diagram overleaf

National Powerboat Course
Level 2 assessment

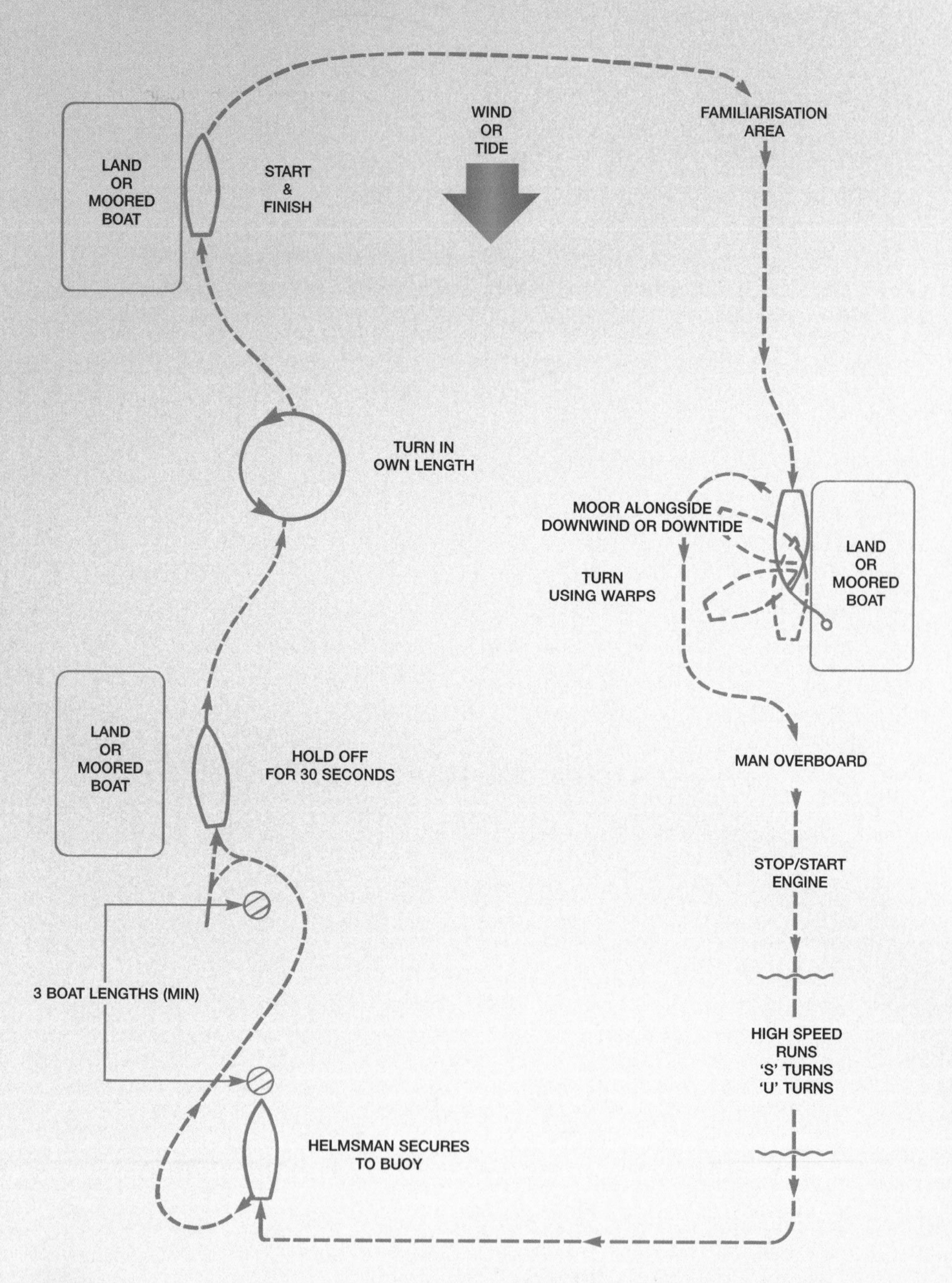

Intermediate Powerboat Day Cruising Course

Aim: To teach powerboating up to the standard required to complete a short coastal passage by day. The ratio of students to instructors should not exceed 6:1 (using two boats).

Assumed knowledge: Candidates should be competent to the standard of National Powerboat Certificate Level 2 with coastal endorsement.

The course will be conducted on a planing boat.

It is strongly recommended that candidates hold a first aid certificate and a VHF operator's certificate.

Duration: 2 days

Minimum age: 16

Section A
Theory

Planning a day cruise

Knowledge of:

- Navigation
- True and magnetic bearings
- Bearing and distance
- Chart symbols
- Tidal diamonds and tidal streams
- Use of pilot books
- Position lines
- Use of marina locks (can be covered practically if appropriate)

Understands:

- Latitude and Longitude
- The principles of GPS
- Sources of forecast information and the interpretation of forecasts
- Tidal heights at secondary ports

Can:

- Use a plotting instrument and plot a course to steer (CTS)
- Work out tidal heights for standard ports using a tidal curve
- Interpret Lateral and Cardinal buoyage
- Implement IRPCS, in particular rules 5, 7, 8, 9, 12-19, 23
- Use GPS waypoint navigation and determine XTE, SOG, COG, BTW, DTW*
- Use a laminated chart afloat
- Use pilotage to enter an unfamiliar port by day
- Explain how to make a VHF emergency call

Signature of Instructor

**XTE - cross track error, SOG - speed over ground, COG - course over ground, BTW - bearing to waypoint, DTW - distance to waypoint*

Section B
Practical

The aim of the practical session is to put into practice the theory detailed above and to complete a passage, which shall include:

Boat Preparation

Understands:

The importance of protective clothing and safety equipment

The minimum level of equipment for the boat

Considerations of equipment required for longer passages

Correct stowage of equipment

Signature of Instructor

Boat handling

Knowledge of:

Effect of waves

Rougher conditions

Awareness of other water users

Mooring stern-to between posts or Med style

Can:

Demonstrate awareness of wind and tide

Moor alongside, in a marina berth (where available)

Demonstrate the use of an appropriate length kill cord at all times

Signature of Instructor

Pilotage

Can:

Demonstrate a practical application of techniques for pilotage in local waters

Signature of Instructor

Passage making

Understands:

The need for pre-planning, including advice in the event of having to return at night

Can:

Apply the lessons learnt in the theory section and successfully complete a practical passage

Fix position by traditional and electronic means

Signature of Instructor

Man overboard

Understands:

Techniques for picking up a man overboard in differing conditions

Can:

Pick up a man overboard

Signature of Instructor

Advanced Powerboat Day and Night Course

Aim: To teach boat handling, seamanship, pilotage and navigation up to the standards required to drive a planing powerboat safely by day and night in tidal coastal waters with which the candidate may be familiar. The ratio of students to instructors should not exceed 6:1 (using two boats). The course will be conducted on a planing powerboat with lights conforming to the IRPCS. Students must wear a minimum 150 Newton lifejacket with a MCA approved light for the night exercise.

Assumed knowledge: Candidates should be competent to the standard of the Intermediate Powerboat Certificate with a thorough knowledge of navigation and chartwork to the level of the Day Skipper Shorebased certificate.

You are required to hold a first aid certificate and a VHF operator's certificate.

Duration: 2 days

Minimum age: 17

Practical

Preparation for sea

Can:

Prepare the powerboat

Carry out fuel and engine checks

Stow and secure gear

Signature of Instructor

Boat handling

Knowledge of:

Differences for a twin engine vessel

Understands:

Characteristics of various hull forms and propeller configurations

Action to be taken in rough weather

Can:

Demonstrate a practical understanding and correct use of power trim and trim tabs

Demonstrate an awareness of the effects of wind and tide when manoeuvring, including:

Steering to transits and in buoyed channels

Turning in a confined space

Berthing in various conditions of wind and tide.

Picking up and leaving a mooring buoy

Demonstrate the use of an appropriate length kill cord at all times

Signature of Instructor

continued overleaf

Passage making and responsibility as skipper

Understands:

The importance of pre-trip planning

Planning and making coastal passages, taking into account the relevant navigational hazards, the type of boat and the strengths of the crew

Chart plotters and radar, their advantages and limitations

Can:

Organise the navigation, safety and welfare of the crew during a powerboat passage

Navigate at higher speed using time/distance

Use electronic navigational equipment for planning and undertaking a passage, including the use of waypoints, routes and XTE, SOG, COG, BTW, DTW*

Signature of Instructor

Pilotage

Can:

Carry out pilotage plans and pilotage for entry into or departure from harbour

Use leading and clearing lines, transits, back bearings and soundings as aids to pilotage

Use GPS and understand its limitations in pilotage

Navigate using soundings

Signature of Instructor

Meteorology

Knowledge of:

Terms used in shipping forecasts, including the Beaufort scale, and their significance to small craft

Understands:

Sources of forecast information and interpretation of forecasts including synoptic charts

The significance of meteorological trends

Can interpret a Synoptic chart

Signature of Instructor

Rules of the Road

Can:

Apply the International Regulations for Preventing Collisions at Sea

Signature of Instructor

**XTE - cross track error, SOG - speed over ground, COG - course over ground, BTW - bearing to waypoint, DTW - distance to waypoint*

Use of engines

Knowledge of:

How to change a propeller

Propeller diameter and pitch

Propeller ventilation and cavitation

Understands:

Checks to be made before starting, during running, and after stopping for diesel and petrol engines

Periodic checks on engines and electrical system including spark plugs, water filters and pump impellers

How to bleed the fuel system (diesel), change filters and pump impellers
Transmission belts

Spares to be carried

Signature of Instructor

Emergency situations

Understands:

Correct action to take in emergency situations

Fire prevention and fighting

Hull damage/watertight integrity

What to do in a medical emergency

Towing and being towed

Helicopter rescue procedures

Use of flares

Search patterns

Can:

Pick up a man overboard in all available conditions

Signature of Instructor

Night cruising

Can:

Take charge of a powerboat at night, including leaving and entering harbour

Demonstrate ability at keeping a proper lookout and identifying lit and unlit marks by night

Signature of Instructor

Safety Boat Course

Aim: to introduce the techniques used in powerboats escorting racing fleets of dinghies and windsurfers, providing safety and rescue cover for training fleets, and assisting in race management. Techniques for canoes/kayaks and kite surfers should also be discussed. It is strongly recommended that a member of the rescue crew should hold a first aid certificate (or should have experience of first aid). The ratio of students to instructors should not exceed 6:1 (using two boats).

Eligibility: RYA Level 2 National Powerboat Certificate

Duration: 2 days

Minimum age: 16

Section A

Practical

Preparation

Understands:

Boat checks

Safety equipment including kill cord management, sharp knife and first aid kit

Crew communication

Race management duties including marking abandoned boats

Signature of Instructor

Boat handling

Understands:

Positioning in respect to fleet

Size of sailing area and response times for different craft

Communication with other craft

Race management duties

Can:

Stand off another craft

Come alongside under way – other powerboats and sailing craft

Lay and recover marks

Demonstrate the correct use of an appropriate length kill cord at all times

Signature of Instructor

Dinghy rescue

Understands:

Methods for recovering personnel from water and techniques for lifting heavy casualties

continued overleaf

How to deal with entrapments

How to right a multihull

Procedures for righting high performance dinghies

The dangers of lee shores

Can:

Approach capsized craft and boats in need of assistance

Right capsized and inverted or partially inverted dinghies, both crewed and single handers

Signature of Instructor

Windsurfer rescue

Understands:

Recovering several boards

Can:

Demonstrate the correct approach

Recover personnel from water

Rescue single board without de-rigging

Stow rigs

Signature of Instructor

Kayak or Canoe rescue (can be covered as theory)

Knowledge of:

The correct approach

How to rescue different types of kayak and canoe

How to return the paddler to his kayak or canoe

How to stow empty kayaks

Towing occupied and empty kayaks or canoes

Signature of Instructor

Towing

Understands:

Length of tow line

Multiple tows

Towing fragile high performance boats

Can:

Tow alongside

Position to pass a tow line

Pass a tow line

Use a bridle

Cast off a tow

Signature of Instructor

End-of-day procedures

Understands:

Refuelling including risks from static electricity and mobile phones

Returning equipment

Reporting faults and problems

Signature of Instructor

Section B

Theory

Safety

Understands:

Use of VHF

Use of tower or club race box for improved vision

First aid

How to carry out a search

Operating from a beach or in shallow water

Signature of Instructor

Suitability of craft

Knowledge of:

Limitations of craft with high freeboard

Hull types

Drive types

Signature of Instructor

Local factors

Knowledge of:

Byelaws and regulations

Signature of Instructor

Communication

Understands:

Crew communication

Communication with other vessels

Signature of Instructor

Rescuing other water users

Knowledge of:

How to rescue swimmers, rowing (sculling) boats, water-skiers and towed inflatables, personal watercraft, canoeists and larger craft

Special considerations for dealing with kite surfers

Signature of Instructor

RECOMMENDED READING

The aim of this logbook is to introduce you to the sport of powerboating and help you gain competence and confidence.

By now, you will probably want to learn more – about engines, boat handling and possibly even navigation. Libraries and chandlers are full of books on boating, but the ones below are particularly recommended.

RYA Weather Handbook

ISBN 0 901501 95 6

This handbook will guide you through the intricacies of weather, explaining how to interpret area weather forecasts, modifying them for local conditions, and by adding observations, improve their accuracy.

RYA Navigation Handbook

ISBN 0 901501 93 X

This book explains the mysteries of direction finding in simple, easy-to-follow stages. It is highly recommended for anyone who needs to navigate safely and confidently, coastal or offshore.

RYA Navigation Exercises

ISBN 0 901501 94 8

An invaluable selection of practice exercises with answers, including position plotting, tidal calculations and passage planning.

Powerboating Practical Course Notes

ISBN 0 901501 77 8

Supports the National Powerboat Scheme with clear diagrams and explanations of the skills covered in the practical courses.

Boat Safety Handbook

ISBN 0 901501 55 7

Useful advice and information on equipment to carry on board for the safety of yourself and your crew. Includes RYA recommendations for life jackets, flares, liferafts, anchor chain etc. Used by the RNLI's Sea Check service.

RYA Powerboat Handbook

ISBN 0 901501 99 9

To be published Summer 2004

The comprehensive powerboating handbook for those wishing to go afloat. This book has been tailored to cover the full National Powerboat Scheme, as revised in 2004.

EXAMINATIONS FOR THE RYA/MCA ADVANCED CERTIFICATE OF COMPETENCE

The Advanced Powerboat Examination is a practical test of boat handling and pilotage. It includes an oral and written test on passage planning, chart work, tides, collision regulations, weather and safety. At least some of the test must be undertaken at night.

The previous experience required before taking this examination, and the scope of the syllabus, is shown on the following pages. There is no requirement to attend a course at a training centres before the exam, although many candidates will find it helpful to brush up their skills at a centre. Skippers should ensure that they are familiar with the handling and other characteristics of any vessel they take to sea.

Certificates of Competence are not required in UK waters on board British flagged pleasure vessels of less than 24 metres load line length, or less than 80 gross tonnes.

Vessels under 24m in length used for sport or recreation on a commercial basis

Vessels used for sport or recreation on a commercial basis are subject to Merchant Shipping legislation. The use of the Advanced Certificate of Competence is permitted for the skippers of these vessels, provided that the certificate is endorsed 'Valid for pleasure vessels up to 24m in length used for commercial purposes'.

To obtain this endorsement an applicant must obtain a Medical Fitness Certificate and attend a Basic Sea Survival Course. Medical Fitness forms and details of the Basic Sea Survival Course are available from the RYA or www.rya.org.uk.

The endorsement for commercial use is valid for five years. It may be renewed by providing evidence of continuing satisfactory service at sea as skipper or mate of a small commercial vessel and a Medical Fitness Certificate.

Withdrawal of Certificates

The RYA's Qualification Panel reserves the right the withdraw certificates at any time if due cause is shown.

Own boat exams

For the exam the candidate must provide a seaworthy vessel capable of a minimum of 12 knots, equipped as laid down in the Notes for Candidates, available from the RYA or www.rya.org.uk. The vessel must be efficiently crewed as the examiner will not take part in the management of the vessel during the exam.

All candidates must wear a 150 or 275 Newton lifejacket with a MCA(UK) approved lifejacket light.

Booking an examination

Advanced Powerboat exams can be booked through our website www.rya.org.uk.

Examinations for service personnel are also conducted by the JSASTC, RNSA, RAFSA and ASA. Servicemen should consult the JSASTC or their Sailing Association for details of examination arrangements.

Exams through a training centre

If you take an Advanced course at an RYA recognised training centre, the exam can be arranged through the centre.

Exams outside the UK

Overseas examinations must be organised through an RYA recognised training centre which is recognised to run the Advanced Powerboat course. The centre must notify the RYA of any overseas exams and the location must be approved by the RYA.

Exams in New Zealand are organised through CBES:

Coastguard Boating Education Service
2 Fred Thomas Drive, Takapuna, Auckland, New Zealand jan@cbes.org.uk

Exam duration

1 candidate	4 - 5 hours
2 candidates	5 - 6 hours
3 Candidates	6 - 7 hours

No more than three candidates can be examined in one session.

Pre-exam requirements

Minimum Seatime required:

- 2 years relevant experience including night pilotage. (As a guide 30 days, 2 days as skipper, 800 miles, 12 night hours).

  If you hold an RYA Advanced Powerboat Course Completion Certificate the seatime is reduced to: 20 days, 2 days as skipper, 400 miles, 12 night hours)

Also required:

- A passport photo
- A copy of your VHF/SRC operator's licence
- A copy of your valid first aid certificate

If you wish to add a commercial endorsement to your certificate you will also need:

- A copy of your Sea Survival certificate
- A completed ML5 medical report

Recommended training prior to examination:

- RYA Level 2 Powerboat Certificate or equivalent knowledge
- RYA Intermediate Powerboat Certificate or equivalent knowledge
- RYA Day Skipper shorebased navigation course completion certificate, or equivalent knowledge
- RYA Advanced Powerboat Course Completion Certificate.

SYLLABUS FOR ADVANCED POWERBOAT EXAMINATION

1 Preparation for sea

- Preparation of Vessel
- Safety brief
- Stowing and securing gear for coastal passages
- Engine operations and routine checks, fuel systems, kill cord
- Fuel system, bleeding, changing filters and impellers

2 Boat handling

- Hull forms and their handling characteristics, propeller configurations.
- Knowledge of action to be taken in rough weather
- Significance of tidal stream on sea conditions
- Steering and power control through waves
- Understanding and correct use of power trim and tabs
- Towing, under open sea conditions and in confined areas
- Strategy up and downwind and in heavy weather

Awareness of the effects of wind and tide when manoeuvring, including:

- Steering to transits and in buoyed channels
- Turning in a confined space
- All berthing and un-berthing
- Picking up and leaving a mooring buoy
- Anchoring
- Recovery of man overboard
- Awareness of ground speed and ability to hold the boat on station

3 Responsibilities of skipper

- Skippering the vessel with effective crew communication
- Preparing the vessel for sea and for adverse weather
- Tactics for heavy weather and restricted visibility
- Emergency and distress situations
- Customs procedures
- Courtesy to other water users

4 Passage making and Pilotage

Your chart work and theory knowledge should include:

- Charts, navigational publications and sources of navigational information
- Chart work, including position fixing and shaping course to allow for tide
- Tidal heights and depths
- Buoyage and visual aids to navigation
- Instruments, including compasses, logs, echo sounders, radio navigation aids and chart work instruments
- Passage planning and navigational tactics
- Importance of pre-planning
- High speed navigation, pre-planning and execution
- Use of electronic navigation (GPS & Radar)
- Pilotage techniques and plans for entry into or departure from harbour
- Use of leading and clearing lines, transits and soundings as aids to pilotage.

- Navigational records
- Limits of navigational accuracy and margins of safety
- Lee shore dangers

You should be able to enter and depart from a charted port by day or night. Your Examiner will give you a pilotage exercise and ask you to explain your planning. You will need to be aware of the problems of collision avoidance and how to determine your position by night.

5 Meteorology

You should be able to use weather and tidal information to predict likely sea conditions and make passage planning decisions.

- Definition of terms including the Beaufort Scale, and their significance to small craft.
- Sources of weather forecasts
- Weather systems and local weather effects
- Interpretation of weather forecasts, barometric trends and visible phenomena
- Ability to make passage planning decisions based on forecast information

6 Rules of the Road

Application of the International Regulations for Preventing Collisions at Sea.

You should be able to identify power and sailing vessels by night. Identification of types of ship by night is not required, but you will need a knowledge of the lights of tugs and trawlers.

7 Safety

Candidates will be expected to know what safety equipment should be carried on board the vessel, based either on the recommendations in RYA booklet C8, or the Codes of Practice for the Safety of Small Commercial Vessels. In particular, candidates must know the responsibilities of a skipper in relation to:

- Fire prevention and fighting
- Hull damage/watertight integrity
- Medical emergency
- Towing and being towed
- VHF emergency procedures
- Explanation of helicopter rescue procedures
- Use of flares
- Man overboard
- Sector search
- Lifejackets
- Life rafts

Summary of experience - prior to record in this logbook

Year	Boat Type planing, displacement semi-displacement	Power Unit outboard.....hp, diesel inboard, outdrive	Hours as Driver	Details of passage, weather, distance covered
08	PLANING	50-75 HP	10	VARIOUS

Personal log

Date	Boat Type planing, displacement semi-displacement	Power Unit outboard.....hp, diesel inboard, outdrive	Hours as Driver	Details of passage, weather, distance covered

Personal log

Date	Boat Type planing, displacement semi-displacement	Power Unit outboard.....hp, diesel inboard, outdrive	Hours as Driver	Details of passage, weather, distance covered

Personal log

Date	Boat Type planing, displacement semi-displacement	Power Unit outboard.....hp, diesel inboard, outdrive	Hours as Driver	Details of passage, weather, distance covered

Personal log

Date	Boat Type planing, displacement semi-displacement	Power Unit outboard.....hp, diesel inboard, outdrive	Hours as Driver	Details of passage, weather, distance covered

Personal log

Date	Boat Type planing, displacement semi-displacement	Power Unit outboard.....hp, diesel inboard, outdrive	Hours as Driver	Details of passage, weather, distance covered

PLEASE ATTACH YOUR RYA LEVEL 1 CERTIFICATE HERE

Please note that no record of certificates is held by the RYA

Enquiries about lost certificates should be made to the centre where the course was taken

PLEASE ATTACH YOUR RYA LEVEL 2 CERTIFICATE HERE

Please note that no record of certificates is held by the RYA

Enquiries about lost certificates should be made to the centre where the course was taken

PLEASE ATTACH YOUR RYA INTERMEDIATE CERTIFICATE HERE

Please note that no record of certificates is held by the RYA

Enquiries about lost certificates should be made to the centre where the course was taken

PLEASE ATTACH YOUR RYA ADVANCED CERTIFICATE HERE

Please note that no record of certificates is held by the RYA

Enquiries about lost certificates should be made to the centre where the course was taken

PLEASE ATTACH YOUR RYA SAFETY BOAT CERTIFICATE HERE

Please note that no record of certificates is held by the RYA

Enquiries about lost certificates should be made to the centre where the course was taken

PLEASE ATTACH YOUR RYA FIRST AID CERTIFICATE HERE

Please note that no record of certificates is held by the RYA

Enquiries about lost certificates should be made to the centre where the course was taken

RYA Membership

Promoting and Protecting Boating
www.rya.org.uk

RYA Membership

Promoting and Protecting Boating

The RYA is the national organisation which represents the interests of everyone who goes boating for pleasure.

The greater the membership, the louder our voice when it comes to protecting members' interests.

Apply for membership today, and support the RYA, to help the RYA support you.

Benefits of Membership

- Access to expert advice on all aspects of boating from legal wrangles to training matters
- Special members' discounts on a range of products and services including boat insurance, books, videos and class certificates
- Free issue of certificates of competence, increasingly asked for by everyone from overseas governments to holiday companies, insurance underwriters to boat hirers
- Access to the wide range of RYA publications, including the quarterly magazine
- Third Party insurance for windsurfing members
- Free Internet access with RYA-Online
- Special discounts on AA membership
- Regular offers in RYA Magazine
- ...and much more

Join now - membership form opposite

Join online at www.rya.org.uk

Visit our website for information, advice, members' services and web shop.

1 Important To help us comply with Data Protection legislation, please tick ***either*** Box A or Box B (you must tick Box A to ensure you receive the full benefits of RYA membership). The RYA will not pass your data to third parties.

☐ **A.** I wish to join the RYA and receive future information on member services, benefits (as listed in RYA Magazine and website) and offers.

☐ **B.** I wish to join the RYA but do not wish to receive future information on member services, benefits (as listed in RYA Magazine and website) and offers.

When completed, please send this form to: RYA, RYA House, Ensign Way, Hamble, Southampton, SO31 4YA

2

	Title	Forename	Surname	Date of Birth	Male	Female
1.				DD / MM / YY		
2.				DD / MM / YY		
3.				DD / MM / YY		
4.				DD / MM / YY		

Address

Town **County** **Post Code**

Evening Telephone **Daytime Telephone**

email **Signature:** ________ **Date:** ________

3 Type of membership required: *(Tick Box)*

☐ ***Personal*** *Current full annual rate £33 or £30 by Direct Debit*
From Ist October 2007 annual rste £39 or £36 by Direct Debit

☐ ***Under 21*** *Current full annual rate £11 (no reduction for Direct Debit)*
From Ist October 2007 will be £13

☐ ***Family**** *Current full annual rate £50 or £47 by Direct Debit*
From Ist October 2007 annual rate £58 or £54 by Direct Debit

** Family Membership: 2 adults plus any under 21s all living at the same address*

Please see Direct Debit form overleaf

4 Please tick ONE box to show your main boating interest.

☐ Yacht Racing ☐ Yacht Cruising
☐ Dinghy Racing ☐ Dinghy Cruising
☐ Personal Watercraft ☐ Inland Waterways
☐ Powerboat Racing ☐ Windsurfing
☐ Motor Boating ☐ Sportsboats and RIBs

Instructions to your Bank or Building Society to pay by Direct Debit

Please complete this form and return it to:
Royal Yachting Association, RYA House, Ensign Way, Hamble, Southampton, Hampshire SO31 4YA

To The Manager: Bank/Building Society

Address:

Post Code:

2. Name(s) of account holder(s)

3. Branch Sort Code

		—			—		

4. Bank or Building Society account number

Originators Identification Number

9	5	5	2	1	3

5. RYA Membership Number (For office use only)

6. Instruction to pay your Bank or Building Society
Please pay Royal Yachting Association Direct Debits from the account detailed in this instruction subject to the safeguards assured by The Direct Debit Guarantee.
I understand that this instruction may remain with the Royal Yachting Association and, if so, details will be passed electronically to my Bank/Building Society.

Signature(s) ____________________

Date ____________________

Banks and Building Societies may not accept Direct Debit instructions for some types of account

Cash, Cheque, Postal Order enclosed £
Made payable to the Royal Yachting Association

077

Office use only: Membership Number Allocated

Office use / Centre Stamp